THE PUFFIN BOOK (

This is an immensely enjoyable and accessible collection, which draws together well-known traditional hymns with more modern favourites to reflect our rich cultural heritage.

The collection has been usefully divided into subsections to help everyone find the right hymn for the right occasion. There are hymns to take you through the day from morning to evening, hymns especially for the family, hymns in praise of nature and those for quiet moments. There are also general hymns of praise and those which are for more specific times of the year, like Easter and Christmas.

The hymns are clearly marked and easy to find. They have been chosen by children, for children, making it an ideal book for use both at home and at school and an obvious companion to *The Puffin Book of Prayers*.

THE PUFFIN BOOK OF
HYMNS

PUFFIN BOOKS

PUFFIN BOOKS
Published by the Penguin Group
Penguin Books Ltd, 27 Wrights Lane, London W8 5TZ, England
Penguin Books USA Inc., 375 Hudson Street, New York, New York 10014, USA
Penguin Books Australia Ltd, Ringwood, Australia
Penguin Books Canada Ltd, 10 Alcorn Avenue, Toronto, Ontario, Canada M4V 3B2
Penguin Books (NZ) Ltd, 182–190 Wairau Road, Auckland 10, New Zealand

Penguin Books Ltd, Registered Offices: Harmondsworth, Middlesex, England

First published 1992
1 3 5 7 9 10 8 6 4 2

Filmset in Monophoto Palatino

Made and printed in Great Britain by
Clays Ltd, St Ives plc

Contents

From the Rising of the Sun
HYMNS THROUGH THE DAY

1   Father, we thank Thee for the night   13

2   From the rising of the sun   13

3   Glory to You, my God, this night   14

4   If I had a hammer   15

5   Lord of all hopefulness   16

6   Now the day is over   17

7   When lamps are lighted in the town   18

Jesus, Friend of Little Children
HYMNS FOR THE FAMILY

8   Gentle Jesus, meek and mild   20

9   Jesus, friend of little children   21

10   Jesus, good above all other   22

11   Jesus loves me! this I know   22

12	Just as I am	23
13	Praise Him, praise Him	24
14	The ink is black	25

For the Beauty of the Earth
HYMNS IN PRAISE OF NATURE AND HARVEST

15	All creatures of our God and King	29
16	All things bright and beautiful	31
17	Come, ye thankful people, come	32
18	Daisies are our silver	34
19	For the beauty of the earth	36
20	God who made the earth	37
21	He's got the whole world in His hand	38
22	Let us, with a gladsome mind	39
23	Morning has broken	40
24	Thank you for the world so sweet	41
25	Twinkle, twinkle, little star	41
26	We plough the fields, and scatter	42

Amazing Grace
HYMNS FOR QUIET MOMENTS

| 27 | Amazing grace! | 45 |

CONTENTS

28	Father, hear the prayer we offer	46
29	Firmly I believe and truly	47
30	Kum ba yah	48
31	Lord Jesus Christ	48
32	Loving Shepherd of Thy sheep	50
33	Praise God from whom all blessings flow	50
34	Psalm 23 – The Lord's my Shepherd	51
35	Put your hand in the hand of the man	53
36	The King of love my Shepherd is	54
37	The Lord's Prayer	55
38	When I needed a neighbour	56

Praise, My Soul, the King of Heaven
HYMNS OF PRAISE

39	All people that on earth do dwell	59
40	At the name of Jesus	60
41	Clap your hands	62
42	Jerusalem	63
43	Joshua fit the battle of Jericho	63
44	Let all the world in ev'ry corner sing	64
45	Lord of the Dance	66
46	Now thank we all our God	68

47	Praise, my soul, the King of heaven	69
48	Oh! how good is the Lord	70
49	The National Anthem	71
50	The two fatherlands	72
51	Tell out, my soul, the greatness of the Lord	73
52	The wise man built his house upon the rock	74
53	When Israel was in Egypt's land	75

Go Tell It on the Mountain
SPREADING THE WORD

54	Colours of day	79
55	Fight the good fight	80
56	Give me oil in my lamp	81
57	Go, tell it on the mountain	83
58	He who would valiant be	84
59	Lead us, heavenly Father, lead us	85
60	Mine eyes have seen the glory	86
61	O when the saints go marching in	88
62	Onward, Christian soldiers	89
63	Stand up! – stand up for Jesus!	90
64	When a knight won his spurs	92

There Is a Green Hill Far Away
HYMNS FOR LENT AND EASTER

65	On Calvary's tree He died for me	95
66	Ride on! ride on in majesty!	95
67	There is a green hill far away	96
68	When I survey the wondrous Cross	97
69	He is Lord	98
70	Jesus Christ is risen today	99
71	Now the green blade rises	101
72	Thine be the glory	102

Infant Holy, Infant Lowly
ADVENT HYMNS AND CHRISTMAS CAROLS

73	Hills of the North, rejoice	105
74	O come, O come, Emmanuel	106
75	Angels from the realms of glory	107
76	Away in a manger	108
77	Ding dong! Merrily on high	109
78	Hark! The herald-angels sing	110
79	I saw three ships	111
80	Infant holy	113

CONTENTS

81	In the bleak mid-winter	114
82	O little town of Bethlehem	115
83	Once in royal David's city	117
84	Rocking carol	118
85	See amid the winter's snow	119
86	Silent night	120
87	The Coventry carol	121
88	The holly and the ivy	121
89	Unto us a Boy is born!	123
90	We three kings of Orient are	124
	Index of first lines	125
	Acknowledgements	128

From the Rising of the Sun

HYMNS THROUGH THE DAY

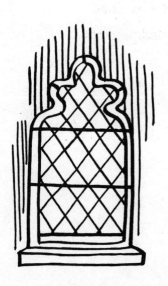

1 Father, we thank Thee for the night

1 Father, we thank Thee for the night,
   And for the pleasant morning light,
   For rest and food, and loving care,
   And all that makes the day so fair.

2 Help us to do the things we should,
   To be to others kind and good,
   In all we do, at work, or play,
   To grow more loving every day.

2 From the rising of the sun

1 From the rising of the sun
   To the going down of the same
   The Lord's name
   Is to be praised.

2 Praise ye the Lord,
   Praise Him O ye servants of the Lord,
   Praise the name of the Lord,
   Blessed be the name of the Lord
   From this time forth,
   And for evermore.

Paul Deming

3   Glory to You, my God, this night

1   Glory to You, my God, this night
For all the blessings of the light;
Keep me, O keep me, King of kings,
Beneath Your own almighty wings.

2   Forgive me, Lord, through Your dear Son,
The wrong that I this day have done,
That peace with God and man may be,
Before I sleep, restored to me.

T. Ken

4   If I had a hammer

1   If I had a hammer, I'd hammer in the morning,
I'd hammer in the evening, all over this land;
I'd hammer out danger, I'd hammer out a
    warning,
I'd hammer out love between my brothers
    and my sisters,
All over this land.

2   If I had a bell, I'd ring it in the morning,
I'd ring it in the evening, all over this land;
I'd ring out danger, I'd ring out a warning,
I'd ring out love between my brothers and my sisters,
All over this land.

3   If I had a song, I'd sing it in the morning,
I'd sing it in the evening, all over this land;
I'd sing out danger, I'd sing out a warning,
I'd sing out love between my brothers and my sisters,
All over this land.

4   Well, I've got a hammer, and I've got a bell,
And I'm going to sing, all over this land;
It's the hammer of justice, it's the bell of freedom,
It's the song about love between my brothers and my
    sisters,
All over this land.

Lee Hays

5   Lord of all hopefulness

1   Lord of all hopefulness, Lord of all joy,
Whose trust, ever childlike, no cares could destroy,
Be there at our waking, and give us, we pray,
Your bliss in our hearts, Lord, at the break of the day.

2   Lord of all eagerness, Lord of all faith,
Whose strong hands were skilled at the plane and the
   lathe,
Be there at our labours, and give us, we pray,
Your strength in our hearts, Lord, at the noon of the
   day.

3   Lord of all kindliness, Lord of all grace,
Your hands swift to welcome, Your arms to embrace,
Be there at our homing, and give us, we pray,
Your love in our hearts, Lord, at the eve of the day.

4   Lord of all gentleness, Lord of all calm,
Whose voice is contentment, whose presence is balm,
Be there at our sleeping, and give us, we pray,
Your peace in our hearts, Lord, at the end of the day.

Jan Struther

6   Now the day is over

1   Now the day is over,
    Night will soon be here,
    Help me to remember
    You are always near.

2   As the darkness gathers,
    Stars shine overhead,
    Creatures, birds and flowers
    Rest their weary heads.

3   Father, give all people
    Calm and peaceful rest,
    Through Your gracious presence
    May our sleep be blessed.

4   Comfort every sufferer
    Watching late in pain;
    Those who plan some evil
    From their sin restrain.

5   When the morning wakes me,
    Ready for the day,
    Help me, Lord, to serve You,
    Walking in Your way.

6   Glory to the Father,
    Glory to the Son;
    And the Holy Spirit
    Blessing everyone.

S. Baring-Gould

7 When lamps are lighted in the town

1   When lamps are lighted in the town,
The boats sail out to sea.
The fishers watch when night comes down,
They work for you and me.

2   We little children go to rest.
Before we sleep, we pray
That God will bless the fishermen
And bring them back at day.

M. M. Penstone

Jesus, Friend of Little Children

HYMNS FOR THE FAMILY

8   Gentle Jesus, meek and mild

1   Gentle Jesus, meek and mild,
    Look upon a little child;
    Pity my simplicity,
    Suffer me to come to Thee.

2   Lamb of God, I look to Thee;
    Thou shalt my example be:
    Thou art gentle, meek and mild,
    Thou wast once a little child.

3   Loving Jesus, gentle Lamb,
    In Thy gracious hands I am:
    Make me, Saviour, what Thou art;
    Live Thyself within my heart.

Charles Wesley

9 Jesus, friend of little children

1 Jesus, friend of little children,
   Be a friend to me;
   Take my hand and ever keep me
   Close to Thee.

2 Teach me how to grow in goodness,
   Daily as I grow;
   Thou has been a child, and surely,
   Thou dost know.

3   Never leave me, nor forsake me,
     Ever be my friend;
     For I need Thee from life's dawning
     To its end.

Walter John Mathams

10   Jesus, good above all other

1   Jesus, good above all other,
     Gentle child of gentle mother,
     In a stable born our brother,
     Give us grace to persevere.

2   Jesus, who our sorrows bearest,
     All our thoughts and hopes Thou sharest,
     Thou to man the truth declarest;
     Help us all Thy truth to hear.

3   Lord, in all our doings guide us;
     Pride and hate shall ne'er divide us;
     We'll go on with Thee beside us,
     And with joy we'll persevere.

Percy Dearmer

11   Jesus loves me! this I know

1   Jesus loves me! this I know,
     For the Bible tells me so;
     Little ones to Him belong;
     They are weak, but He is strong.

Yes! Jesus loves me!
Yes! Jesus loves me!
Yes! Jesus loves me!
The Bible tells me so.

2 Jesus loves me! He who died
   Heaven's gate to open wide;
   He will wash away my sin,
   Let His little child come in:

3 Jesus loves me! He will stay
   Close beside me all the way;
   Then His little child will take
   Up to heaven, for His dear sake:

Anna Warner

12   Just as I am

1 Just as I am, Your child to be,
   Friend of the young, who died for me;
   To give my life whole-heartedly,
   O Jesus Christ, I come.

2 While I am still a child today,
   I give my life, my work and play
   To Him alone, without delay,
   With all my heart I come.

3   I see in Jesus Christ the light,
    With Him as Lord, and in His might
    I turn from sin to what is right,
    My Lord, to You I come.

4   Lord, take my dreams of fame and gold,
    I accept now a life controlled
    By faith in You as days unfold,
    With my whole life I come.

5   Just as I am, young, strong and free,
    To be the best that I can be,
    That others may see You in me,
    Lord of my life I come.

Marianne Farningham

13   Praise Him, praise Him

1   Praise Him, praise Him, all you little children,
    God is love, God is love.
    Praise Him, praise Him, all you little children,
    God is love, God is love.

2   Love Him, love Him, all you little children,
    God is love, God is love.
    Love Him, love Him, all you little children,
    God is love, God is love.

3   Thank Him, thank Him, all you little children,
    God is love, God is love.
    Thank Him, thank Him, all you little children,
    God is love, God is love.

14   The ink is black

1   The ink is black, the page is white,
   Together we learn to read and write, to read and
      write;
   And now a child can understand
   This is the law of all the land, all the land;
   The ink is black, the page is white,
   Together we learn to read and write, to read and
      write.

2   The slate is black, the chalk is white,
   The words stand out so clear and bright, so clear and
      bright;
   And now at last we plainly see
   The alphabet of liberty, liberty;
   The slate is black, the chalk is white,
   Together we learn to read and write, to read and
      write.

3   A child is black, a child is white,
   The whole world looks upon the sight, upon the
      sight;
   For very well the whole world knows
   This is the way that freedom grows, freedom grows;
   A child is black, a child is white,
   Together we learn to read and write, to read and
      write.

4   The world is black, the world is white,
It turns by day and then by night, and then by night;
It turns so each and every one
Can take his station in the sun, in the sun;
The world is black, the world is white,
Together we learn to read and write, to read and
    write.

David Arkin

For the Beauty of the Earth

HYMNS IN PRAISE OF NATURE AND HARVEST

15 All creatures of our God and King

1 All creatures of our God and King,
   Lift up your voice and with us sing
   Alleluia, Alleluia!
   Thou burning sun with golden beam,
   Thou silver moon with softer gleam,

   O praise Him, O praise Him,
   Alleluia, Alleluia, Alleluia!

2 Thou rushing wind that art so strong,
   Ye clouds that sail in heaven along,
   O praise Him, Alleluia!
   Thou rising moon, in praise rejoice,
   Ye lights of evening, find a voice:

3 Thou flowing water, pure and clear,
   Make music for thy Lord to hear,
   Alleluia, Alleluia!
   Thou fire so masterful and bright,
   That givest man both warmth and light:

4 Dear mother earth, who day by day
   Unfoldest blessings on our way,
   O praise Him, Alleluia!
   The flowers and fruits that in thee grow,
   Let them His glory also show:

5 And all ye men of tender heart,
   Forgiving others, take your part,
   O sing ye, Alleluia!
   Ye who long pain and sorrow bear,
   Praise God and on Him cast your care:

6 And thou most kind and gentle Death,
   Waiting to hush our latest breath,
   O praise Him, Alleluia!
   Thou leadest home the child of God,
   And Christ our Lord the way hath trod:

7 Let all things their Creator bless,
   And worship Him in humbleness,
   O praise Him, Alleluia!
   Praise, praise the Father, praise the Son,
   And praise the Spirit, Three in One:

W. H. Draper

16 All things bright and beautiful

All things bright and beautiful,
All creatures great and small,
All things wise and wonderful,
The Lord God made them all.

1 Each little flower that opens,
   Each little bird that sings,
   He made their glowing colours,
   He made their tiny wings:

2 The rich man in his castle,
   The poor man at his gate,
   God made them, high or lowly,
   And ordered their estate:

3 The purple-headed mountain,
   The river running by,
   The sunset and the morning,
   That brightens up the sky:

4 The cold wind in the winter,
   The pleasant summer sun,
   The ripe fruits in the garden,
   He made them every one:

5 The tall trees in the greenwood,
   The meadows for our play,
   The rushes by the water,
   To gather every day:

6   He gave us eyes to see them,
    And lips that we may tell
    How great is God Almighty,
    Who has made all things well:

Mrs C. F. Alexander

17   Come, ye thankful people, come

1   Come, ye thankful people, come,
    Raise the song of harvest-home:
    All is safely gathered in,
    Ere the winter storms begin;
    God, our Maker, doth provide
    For our wants to be supplied:
    Come to God's own temple, come,
    Raise the song of harvest-home.

2   All this world is God's own field,
    Fruit unto His praise to yield;
    Wheat and tares together sown,
    Unto joy or sorrow grown;
    First the blade, and then the ear,
    Then the full corn shall appear:
    Lord of harvest, grant that we
    Wholesome grain and pure may be.

3   For the Lord our God shall come,
    And shall take His harvest home;
    From His field shall in that day
    All offences purge away;
    Give His angels charge at last
    In the fire the tares to cast;
    But the fruitful ears to store
    In His garner evermore.

4   Even so, Lord, quickly come;
    Bring Thy final harvest home:
    Gather Thou Thy people in,
    Free from sorrow, free from sin;
    There, for ever purified,
    In Thy garner to abide:
    Come, with all Thine angels, come,
    Raise the glorious harvest-home.

H. Alford

18   Daisies are our silver

1   Daisies are our silver,
    Buttercups our gold:
    This is all the treasure
    We can have or hold.

2   Raindrops are our diamonds
    And the morning dew;
    While for shining sapphires
    We've the speedwell blue.

3   These shall be our emeralds –
    Leaves so new and green;
    Roses make the reddest
    Rubies ever seen.

4   God, who gave these treasures
    To Your children small,
    Teach us how to love them
    And grow like them all.

5   Make us bright as silver:
    Make us good as gold;
    Warm as summer roses
    Let our hearts unfold.

6   Gay as leaves in April,
    Clear as drops of dew –
    God, who made the speedwell,
    Keep us true to You.

                              Jan Struther

19   For the beauty of the earth

1   For the beauty of the earth,
    For the beauty of the skies,
    For the love, which from our birth
    Over and around us lies:

    Father, unto Thee we raise
    This our sacrifice of praise.

2   For the beauty of each hour
    Of the day and of the night,
    Hill and vale, and tree and flower,
    Sun and moon and stars of light:

3   For the joy of ear and eye,
    For the heart and brain's delight,
    For the mystic harmony
    Linking sense to sound and sight:

4   For the joy of human love,
    Brother, sister, parent, child,
    Friends on earth, and friends above,
    For all gentle thoughts and mild:

5   For each perfect gift of Thine
    To our race so freely given,
    Graces human and divine,
    Flowers of earth and buds of heaven:

F. S. Pierpoint

20   God who made the earth

1   God who made the earth,
The air, the sky, the sea,
Who gave the light its birth,
Will care for me.

2   God who made the grass,
The flower, the fruit, the tree,
The day and night to pass,
Will care for me.

3   God who made the sun,
The moon, the stars, is He
Who when life's clouds come on,
Will care for me.

4   God who sent His Son
To die on Calvary,
He, if I lean on Him,
Will care for me.

5   God who gave me life,
His servant here to be,
Has promised in His word
To care for me.

S. B. Rhodes

21   He's got the whole world in His hand

He's got the whole world in His hand,
He's got the whole wide world in His hand,
He's got the whole world in His hand,
He's got the whole world in His hand.

1   He's got the wind and the rain in His hand,
He's got the wind and the rain in His hand,
He's got the wind and the rain in His hand,
He's got the whole world in His hand:

2   He's got the sun and the moon in His hand,
He's got the sun and the moon in His hand,
He's got the sun and the moon in His hand,
He's got the whole world in His hand:

3   He's got the plants and the creatures in His hand,
He's got the plants and the creatures in His hand,
He's got the plants and the creatures in His hand,
He's got the whole world in His hand:

4   He's got everybody here in His hand,
He's got everybody here in His hand,
He's got everybody here in His hand,
He's got the whole world in His hand:

Traditional

22   Let us, with a gladsome mind

1   Let us, with a gladsome mind,
Praise the Lord, for He is kind:

*For His mercies ay endure,
Ever faithful, ever sure.*

2   Let us blaze His name abroad,
For of gods He is the God:

3   He with all-commanding might
Filled the new-made world with light:

4   He the golden-tressèd sun
Caused all day His course to run:

5   The hornèd moon to shine by night,
'Mid her spangled sisters bright:

6   All things living He doth feed,
His full hand supplies their need:

7   Let us, with a gladsome mind,
Praise the Lord, for he is kind:

John Milton

23   Morning has broken

1   Morning has broken,
Like the first morning.
Blackbird has spoken,
Like the first bird.
Praise for the singing!
Praise for the morning!
Praise for them, springing
Fresh from the word!

2   Sweet the rain's new fall
Sunlit from heaven,
Like the first dewfall
On the first grass.
Praise for the sweetness
Of the wet garden,
Sprung in completeness
Where His feet pass.

3   Mine is the sunlight!
Mine is the morning
Born of the one light
Eden saw play!
Praise with elation,
Praise every morning,
God's re-creation
Of the new day!

Eleanor Farjeon

24 Thank you for the world so sweet

Thank you for the world so sweet;
Thank you for the food we eat;
Thank you for the birds that sing:
Thank you, God, for everything!

E. Ruther Leatham

25 Twinkle, twinkle, little star

Twinkle, twinkle, little star,
How I wonder what you are,
Up above the world so high,
Like a diamond in the sky.
Twinkle, twinkle, little star,
How I wonder what you are.

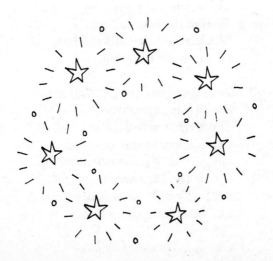

26 We plough the fields, and scatter

1   We plough the fields, and scatter
The good seed on the land,
But it is fed and watered
By God's almighty hand;
He sends the snow in winter,
The warmth to swell the grain,
The breezes and the sunshine,
And soft refreshing rain.

All good gifts around us
Are sent from heav'n above;
Then thank the Lord, O thank the Lord,
For all His love.

2   He only is the Maker
Of all things near and far,
He paints the wayside flower,
He lights the evening star.
The winds and waves obey Him,
By Him the birds are fed;
Much more to us, His children,
He gives our daily bread:

3   We thank Thee then, O Father,
For all things bright and good;
The seed-time and the harvest,
Our life, our health, our food.
No gifts have we to offer
For all Thy love imparts,
But that which Thou desirest,
Our humble, thankful hearts:

M. Claudius, Translated by J. M. Campbell

Amazing Grace

HYMNS FOR QUIET MOMENTS

27 Amazing grace!

1 Amazing grace! how sweet the sound
   That saved a wretch like me!
   I once was lost, but now am found,
   Was blind, but now I see.

2 'Twas grace that taught my heart to fear,
   And grace my fears relieved;
   How precious did that grace appear
   The hour I first believed.

3 Through many dangers, toils, and snares
   I have already come;
   'Tis grace hath brought me safe thus far,
   And grace will lead me home.

4 The Lord has promised good to me,
   His word my hope secures;
   He will my shield and portion be
   As long as life endures.

5 Yes, when this heart and flesh shall fail,
   And mortal life shall cease,
   I shall possess within the veil
   A life of joy and peace.

John Newton

28 Father, hear the prayer we offer

1 Father, hear the prayer we offer:
   Not for ease that prayer shall be,
   But for strength that we may ever
   Live our lives courageously.

2 Not for ever in green pastures
   Do we ask our way to be,
   But the steep and rugged pathway
   May we tread rejoicingly.

3 Not for ever by still waters
   Would we idly rest and stay,
   But would smite the living fountains
   From the rocks along our way.

4 Be our strength in hours of weakness,
   In our wanderings be our guide;
   Through endeavour, failure, danger,
   Father, be Thou at our side.

L. M. Willis and others

29   Firmly I believe and truly

1   Firmly I believe and truly
    God is Three, and God is One;
    And I next acknowledge duly
    Manhood taken by the Son.

2   And I trust and hope most fully
    In that Manhood crucified;
    And each thought and deed unruly
    Do to death, as He has died.

3   Simply to His grace and wholly
    Light and life and strength belong,
    And I love supremely, solely,
    Him the holy, Him the strong.

4   And I hold in veneration,
    For the love of Him alone,
    Holy Church as His creation,
    And her teachings as His own.

5   Adoration aye be given,
    With and through the angelic host,
    To the God of earth and heaven,
    Father, Son, and Holy Ghost.

John Henry Newman

30 Kum ba yah

1   Kum ba yah, my Lord, Kum ba yah,
    Kum ba yah, my Lord, Kum ba yah,
    Kum ba yah, my Lord, Kum ba yah,
    O Lord, Kum ba yah.

2   Someone's crying, Lord, Kum ba yah,
    Someone's crying, Lord, Kum ba yah,
    Someone's crying, Lord, Kum ba yah,
    O Lord, Kum ba yah.

3   Someone's singing, Lord, Kum ba yah,
    Someone's singing, Lord, Kum ba yah,
    Someone's singing, Lord, Kum ba yah,
    O Lord, Kum ba yah.

4   Someone's praying, Lord, Kum ba yah,
    Someone's praying, Lord, Kum ba yah,
    Someone's praying, Lord, Kum ba yah,
    O Lord, Kum ba yah.

Traditional

31 Lord Jesus Christ

1   Lord Jesus Christ,
    You have come to us,
    You are one with us,
    Mary's Son.
    Cleansing our souls from all their sin,
    Pouring Your love and goodness in,
    Jesus, our love for You we sing,
    Living Lord.

2   Lord Jesus Christ,
Now and every day
Teach us how to pray,
Son of God.
You have commanded us to do
This, in remembrance, Lord, of You:
Into our lives Your power breaks through,
Living Lord.

3   Lord Jesus Christ,
You have come to us,
Born as one of us,
Mary's Son.
Led out to die on Calvary,
Risen from death to set us free,
Living Lord Jesus, help us see
You are Lord.

4   Lord Jesus Christ,
I would come to You,
Live my life for You,
Son of God.
All Your commands I know are true,
Your many gifts will make me new,
Into my life Your power breaks through,
Living Lord.

Patrick Appleford

32 Loving Shepherd of Thy sheep

1   Loving Shepherd of Thy sheep,
Keep Thy lamb, in safety keep;
Nothing can Thy power withstand,
None can pluck me from Thy hand.

2   Loving Shepherd, ever near,
Teach Thy lamb Thy voice to hear;
Suffer not my steps to stray
From the strait and narrow way.

3   Where Thou leadest I would go,
Walking in Thy steps below,
Till before my Father's throne
I shall know as I am known.

Jane Eliza Leeson

33 Praise God from whom all blessings flow

Praise God from whom all blessings flow;
Praise Him all creatures here below.
Praise Him above ye heavenly host;
Praise Father, Son, and Holy Ghost.

T. Ken

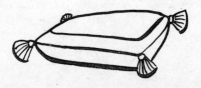

34 Psalm 23 – The Lord's my Shepherd

1   The Lord's my Shepherd, I'll not want.
    He makes me down to lie
    In pastures green; He leadeth me
    The quiet waters by.

2   My soul He doth restore again,
    And me to walk doth make
    Within the paths of righteousness,
    E'en for His own name's sake.

3   Yea, though I walk in death's dark vale,
    Yet will I fear none ill;
    For Thou art with me, and Thy rod
    And staff me comfort still.

4   My table Thou hast furnishèd
    In presence of my foes;
    My head Thou dost with oil anoint,
    And my cup overflows.

5   Goodness and mercy all my life
    Shall surely follow me;
    And in God's house for evermore
    My dwelling-place shall be.

35   Put your hand in the hand of the man

1   Put your hand in the hand of the man who stilled the water.
Put your hand in the hand of the man who calmed the sea.
Take a look at yourself and you can look at others diff'rently,
By puttin' your hand in the hand of the man from Galilee.

2   Ev'rytime I look into the Holy Book I want to tremble
When I read about the part where a carpenter cleared the temple.
For the buyers and the sellers were no diff'rent fellas than what I profess to be,
And it causes me pain to know we're not the people we should be.

3   Put your hand in the hand of the man who stilled the water.
Put your hand in the hand of the man who calmed the sea.
Take a look at yourself and you can look at others diff'rently,
By puttin' your hand in the hand of the man from Galilee.

Gene MacLellan

36 The King of love my Shepherd is

1   The King of love my Shepherd is,
    Whose goodness faileth never;
    I nothing lack if I am His
    And He is mine for ever.

2   Where streams of living water flow
    My ransomed soul He leadeth,
    And where the verdant pastures grow
    With food celestial feedeth.

3   Perverse and foolish oft I strayed,
    But yet in love He sought me,
    And on His shoulder gently laid,
    And home rejoicing brought me.

4   In death's dark vale I fear no ill
    With Thee, dear Lord, beside me;
    Thy rod and staff my comfort still,
    Thy Cross before to guide me.

5   Thou spread'st a table in my sight;
    Thy unction grace bestoweth;
    And O what transport of delight
    From Thy pure chalice floweth!

6   And so through all the length of days
    Thy goodness faileth never:
    Good Shepherd, may I sing Thy praise
    Within Thy house for ever.

Sir Henry Baker

37 The Lord's Prayer

Our Father, who art in heaven,
Hallowed be Thy name;
Thy kingdom come, Thy will be done
Hallowed be Thy name,
On the earth as it is in heaven.
Hallowed be Thy name.
Give us this day our daily bread.
Hallowed be Thy name;
Forgive us all our trespasses,
Hallowed be Thy name,
As we forgive those who trespass against us,
Hallowed be Thy name.
And lead us not into temptation,
Hallowed be Thy name;
But deliver us from all that is evil.
Hallowed be Thy name,
For Thine is the kingdom, the power and the glory,
Hallowed be Thy name.
For ever and for ever and ever,
Hallowed be Thy name;
Amen, Amen, it shall be so,
Hallowed be Thy name,
Amen, Amen, it shall be so.
Hallowed be Thy name.

Traditional Caribbean

38   When I needed a neighbour

1   When I needed a neighbour, were you there, were
       you there?
    When I needed a neighbour, were you there?

    And the creed and the colour and the name won't matter,
    Were you there?

2   I was hungry and thirsty, were you there, were you
       there?
    I was hungry and thirsty, were you there?:

3   I was cold, I was naked, were you there, were you there?
    I was cold, I was naked, were you there?:

4   When I needed a shelter, were you there, were you
       there?
    When I needed a shelter, were you there?:

5   When I needed a healer, were you there, were you
       there?
    When I needed a healer, were you there?:

6   Wherever you travel, I'll be there, I'll be there,
    Wherever you travel, I'll be there.

    And the creed and the colour and the name won't matter,
    I'll be there.

                                                Sydney Carter

Praise, My Soul, the King of Heaven

HYMNS OF PRAISE

39   All people that on earth do dwell

1   All people that on earth do dwell,
    Sing to the Lord with cheerful voice;
    Him serve with fear, His praise forth tell,
    Come ye before Him, and rejoice.

2   The Lord, ye know, is God indeed;
    Without our aid He did us make;
    We are His folk, He doth us feed,
    And for His sheep He doth us take.

3   O enter then His gates with praise,
    Approach with joy His courts unto;
    Praise, laud, and bless His name always,
    For it is seemly so to do.

4   For why? The Lord our God is good;
    His mercy is for ever sure;
    His truth at all times firmly stood,
    And shall from age to age endure.

5   To Father, Son, and Holy Ghost,
    The God whom heaven and earth adore,
    From men and from the angel-host
    Be praise and glory evermore.

William Kethe

40   At the name of Jesus

1   At the name of Jesus
     Every knee shall bow,
     Every tongue confess Him
     King of glory now;
     'Tis the Father's pleasure
     We should call Him Lord,
     Who from the beginning
     Was the mighty word.

2   Mighty and mysterious
     In the highest height,
     God from everlasting,
     Very light of light:
     In the Father's bosom
     With the spirit blest,
     Love, in love eternal,
     Rest, in perfect rest.

3   At His voice creation
     Sprang at once to sight,
     All the angel faces,
     All the hosts of light,
     Thrones and dominations,
     Stars upon their way,
     All the heavenly orders,
     In their great array.

4   Humbled for a season,
    To receive a name
    From the lips of sinners
    Unto whom He came,
    Faithfully He bore it
    Spotless to the last,
    Brought it back victorious
    When from death He passed.

5   Bore it up triumphant
    With its human light,
    Through all ranks of creatures,
    To the central height,
    To the throne of Godhead,
    To the Father's breast;
    Filled it with the glory
    Of that perfect rest.

6   Name Him, brothers, name Him,
    With love as strong as death,
    But with awe and wonder,
    And with bated breath;
    He is God the Saviour,
    He is Christ the Lord,
    Ever to be worshipped,
    Trusted, and adored.

7   In your hearts enthrone Him;
    There let Him subdue
    All that is not holy,
    All that is not true:

Crown Him as your captain
In temptation's hour;
Let His will enfold you
In its light and power.

8   Brothers, this Lord Jesus
Shall return again,
With His Father's glory,
With His angel train;
For all wreaths of empire
Meet upon His brow,
And our hearts confess Him
King of glory now.

Caroline M. Noel and others

41   Clap your hands

Clap your hands all you people,
Shout unto God with a voice of triumph.
Clap your hands all you people,
Shout unto God with a voice of praise!
Hosanna, Hosanna,
Shout unto God with a voice of triumph.
Praise Him, Praise Him,
Shout unto God with a voice of praise!

Jimmy Owens

42   Jerusalem

1   And did those feet in ancient time
Walk upon England's mountains green?
And was the holy Lamb of God
On England's pleasant pastures seen?
And did the countenance divine
Shine forth upon our clouded hills
And was Jerusalem builded here
Among those dark satanic mills?

2   Bring me my bow of burning gold!
Bring me my arrows of desire!
Bring me my spear! O clouds, unfold!
Bring me my chariot of fire!
I will not cease from mental fight,
Nor shall my sword sleep in my hand,
Till we have built Jerusalem
In England's green and pleasant land.

William Blake

43   Joshua fit the battle of Jericho

Joshua fit the battle of Jericho,
Jericho, Jericho,
Joshua fit the battle of Jericho,
And the walls came tumbling down.

1   You may talk about your king of Gideon,
You may talk about your man of Saul,
But there's none like good old Joshua
At the battle of Jericho:

2   Up to the walls of Jericho
    He marched with spear in hand.
    'Go blow them ram-horns,' Joshua cried,
    'Cause the battle am in my hand.':

3   Then the ram-sheep's horns began to blow,
    Trumpets began to sound.
    Joshua commanded the children to shout,
    And the walls came tumbling down, that morning:

44   Let all the world in ev'ry corner sing

1   Let all the world in ev'ry corner sing,
    My God and King!
    The heav'ns are not too high,
    His praise may thither fly;
    The earth is not too low,
    His praises there may grow.
    Let all the world in ev'ry corner sing,
    My God and King!

2   Let all the world in ev'ry corner sing,
    My God and King!
    The Church with psalms must shout,
    No door can keep them out;
    But above all, the heart
    Must bear the longest part.
    Let all the world in ev'ry corner sing,
    My God and King!

George Herbert

45   Lord of the Dance

1   I danced in the morning
    When the world was begun,
    And I danced in the moon
    And the stars and the sun,
    And I came down from heaven
    And I danced on the earth;
    At Bethlehem
    I had my birth.

Dance, then, wherever you may be;
I am the Lord of the Dance, said he,
And I'll lead you all, wherever you may be,
And I'll lead you all in the dance, said he.

2   I danced for the scribe
    And the pharisee,
    But they would not dance
    And they wouldn't follow me;
    I danced for the fishermen,
    For James and John;
    They came with me
    And the dance went on:

3   I danced on the Sabbath
    And I cured the lame:
    The holy people
    Said it was a shame.
    They whipped and they stripped
    And they hung me high,
    And they left me there
    On a cross to die:

4   I danced on a Friday
When the sky turned black;
It's hard to dance
With the devil on your back.
They buried my body
And they thought I'd gone;
But I am the dance
And I still go on:

5   They cut me down
And I leapt up high;
I am the life
That'll never, never die;
I'll live in you
If you'll live in me:
I am the Lord
Of the Dance, said he:

Sydney Carter

46   Now thank we all our God

1   Now thank we all our God,
    With heart and hands and voices,
    Who wondrous things hath done,
    In whom His world rejoices;
    Who from our mother's arms
    Hath blessed us on our way
    With countless gifts of love,
    And still is ours today.

2   O may this bounteous God
    Through all our life be near us,
    With ever joyful hearts
    And blessèd peace to cheer us;
    And keep us in His grace,
    And guide us when perplexed,
    And free us from all ills
    In this world and the next.

3   All praise and thanks to God
    The Father now be given,
    The Son, and Him who reigns
    With them in highest heaven;
    The one eternal God,
    Whom earth and heaven adore,
    For thus it was, is now,
    And shall be evermore.

M. Rinkart
Translated by T. C. Winkworth

47   Praise, my soul, the King of heaven

1   Praise, my soul, the King of heaven;
    To His feet thy tribute bring.
    Ransomed, healed, restored, forgiven,
    Who like me His praise should sing?
    Praise Him! Praise Him!
    Praise Him! Praise Him!
    Praise the everlasting King!

2   Praise Him for His grace and favour
    To our fathers in distress;
    Praise Him still the same for ever,
    Slow to chide, and swift to bless.
    Praise Him! Praise Him!
    Praise Him! Praise Him!
    Glorious in His faithfulness.

3   Father-like, He tends and spares us;
    Well our feeble frame He knows;
    In His hands He gently bears us,
    Rescues us from all our foes.
    Praise Him! Praise Him!
    Praise Him! Praise Him!
    Widely as His mercy flows.

4   Frail as summer's flower we flourish:
    Blows the wind, and it is gone.
    But, while mortals rise and perish,
    God endures unchanging on.
    Praise Him! Praise Him!
    Praise Him! Praise Him!
    Praise the high eternal One!

5   Angels, help us to adore Him;
      Ye behold Him face to face;
      Sun and moon, bow down before Him.
      Dwellers all in time and space.
      Alleluia! Alleluia!
      Praise with us the God of grace!

Henry Francis Lyle

48   Oh! how good is the Lord

Oh! Oh! Oh! how good is the Lord.
Oh! Oh! Oh! how good is the Lord.
Oh! Oh! Oh! how good is the Lord.
I never will forget what He has done for me.

1   He gives me salvation, how good is the Lord.
      He gives me salvation, how good is the Lord.
      He gives me salvation, how good is the Lord.
      I never will forget what He has done for me:

2   He gives me His blessings . . .

3   He gives me His Spirit . . .

4   He gives me His healing . . .

5   He gives me His glory . . .

49 The National Anthem

1   God save our gracious Queen,
    Long live our noble Queen,
    God save the Queen.
    Send her victorious,
    Happy and glorious,
    Long to reign over us:
    God save the Queen.

2   Thy choicest gifts in store
    On her be pleased to pour,
    Long may she reign.
    May she defend our laws,
    And ever give us cause
    To sing with heart and voice,
    God save the Queen.

50   The two fatherlands

1   I vow to thee, my country, all earthly things above,
Entire and whole and perfect, the service of my love;
The love that asks no question, the love that stands
the test,
That lays upon the altar the dearest and the best;
The love that never falters, the love that pays the
price,
The love that makes undaunted the final sacrifice.

2   And there's another country, I've heard of long ago,
Most dear to them that love her, most great to them
that know;
We may not count her armies, we may not see her
King;
Her fortress is a faithful heart, her pride is suffering;
And soul by soul and silently her shining bounds
increase,
And her ways are ways of gentleness and all her
paths are peace.

Sir Cecil Spring Rice

51   Tell out, my soul, the greatness
of the Lord

1   Tell out, my soul, the greatness of the Lord;
Unnumbered blessings, give my spirit voice;
Tender to me the promise of His word;
In God my Saviour shall my heart rejoice.

2   Tell out, my soul, the greatness of His name;
Make known His might, the deeds His arm has done;
His mercy sure, from age to age the same;
His holy name, the Lord, the Mighty One.

3   Tell out, my soul, the greatness of His might;
Powers and dominions lay their glory by,
Proud hearts and stubborn will are put to flight,
The hungry fed, the humble lifted high.

4   Tell out, my soul, the glories of His word;
Firm is his promise, and His mercy sure,
Tell out, my soul, the greatness of the Lord
To children's children and for evermore.

Timothy Dudley-Smith

52   The wise man built his house upon the rock

1   The wise man built his house upon the rock.
The wise man built his house upon the rock.
The wise man built his house upon the rock,
And the rain came tumbling down.
And the rain came down and the floods came up,
The rain came down and the floods came up,
The rain came down and the floods came up,
And the house on the rock stood firm.

2   The foolish man built his house upon the sand.
The foolish man built his house upon the sand.
The foolish man built his house upon the sand,
And the rain came tumbling down.
And the rain came down and the floods came up,
The rain came down and the floods came up,
The rain came down and the floods came up,
And the house on the sand fell flat.

53   When Israel was in Egypt's land

1   When Israel was in Egypt's land,
Let my people go;
Oppressed so hard they could not stand,
Let my people go:

Go down, Moses, way down in Egypt's land;
Tell old Pharaoh to let my people go.

2   The Lord told Moses what to do,
Let my people go;
To lead the children of Israel through,
Let my people go:

3 Your foes shall not before you stand,
   Let my people go;
   And you'll possess fair Canaan's land,
   Let my people go:

4 O let us from all bondage flee,
   Let my people go;
   And let us all in Christ be free,
   Let my people go:

5 I do believe without a doubt,
   Let my people go;
   That a Christian has a right to shout,
   Let my people go:

Negro spiritual
Adapted by Peter D. Smith

Go Tell It on the Mountain

SPREADING THE WORD

54 Colours of day

1 Colours of day dawn into the mind,
   The sun has come up, the night is behind.
   Go down in the city, into the street,
   And let's give the message to the people we meet.

   So light up the fire and let the flame burn,
   Open the door, let Jesus return.
   Take seeds of His Spirit, let the fruit grow,
   Tell the people of Jesus, let His love show.

2 Go through the park, on into the town;
   The sun still shines on, it never goes down.
   The light of the world is risen again;
   The people of darkness are needing our friend:

3 Open your eyes, look into the sky,
   The darkness has come, the sun came to die.
   The evening draws on, the sun disappears,
   But Jesus is living, His Spirit is near:

   Susan McClellan, John Pac and Keith Rycroft

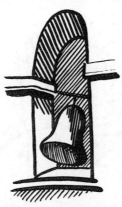

55 Fight the good fight

1 Fight the good fight with all thy might,
   Christ is thy strength, and Christ thy right;
   Lay hold on life, and it shall be
   Thy joy and crown eternally.

2 Run the straight race through God's good grace,
   Lift up thine eyes, and seek His face;
   Life with its way before us lies,
   Christ is the path, and Christ the prize.

3 Cast care aside, upon thy Guide
   Lean, and His mercy will provide;
   Lean, and the trusting soul shall prove
   Christ is its life, and Christ its love.

4 Faint not nor fear, His arms are near,
   He changeth not, and thou art dear;
   Only believe, and thou shalt see
   That Christ is all in all to thee.

J. S. B. Monsell

56   Give me oil in my lamp

1   Give me oil in my lamp, keep me burning.
Give me oil in my lamp, I pray.
Give me oil in my lamp, keep me burning,
Keep me burning till the break of day.

Sing hosanna, sing hosanna,
Sing hosanna to the King of kings!
Sing hosanna, sing hosanna,
Sing hosanna to the King!

2   Give me joy in my heart, keep me singing.
Give me joy in my heart, I pray.
Give me joy in my heart, keep me singing,
Keep me singing till the break of day:

3   Give me love in my heart, keep me serving.
Give me love in my heart, I pray.
Give me love in my heart, keep me serving,
Keep me serving till the break of day:

4   Give me peace in my heart, keep me resting.
Give me peace in my heart, I pray.
Give me peace in my heart, keep me resting,
Keep me resting till the break of day:

Traditional

57   Go, tell it on the mountain

Go, tell it on the mountain,
Over the hills and ev'rywhere;
Go, tell it on the mountain
That Jesus is His name.

1   He possessed no riches, no home to lay His head;
He saw the needs of others and cared for them
    instead:

2   He reached out and touched them, the blind, the deaf,
    the lame;
He spoke and listened gladly to anyone who came:

3   Some turned away in anger, with hatred in the eye;
They tried Him and condemned Him, then led Him
    out to die:

4   'Father, now forgive them' – those were the words
    He said;
In three more days He was alive and risen from the
    dead:

5   He still comes to people, His life moves through the
    lands;
He uses us for speaking, He touches with our hands:

Geoffrey Marshall-Taylor

83

58   He who would valiant be

1   He who would valiant be
'Gainst all disaster,
Let him in constancy
Follow the Master,
There's no discouragement
Shall make him once relent
His first avowed intent
To be a pilgrim.

2   Who so beset him round
With dismal stories,
Do but themselves confound –
His strength the more is.
No foes shall stay his might,
Though he with giants fight:
He will make good his right
To be a pilgrim.

3   Since, Lord, thou dost defend
Us with Thy Spirit,
We know we at the end
Shall life inherit.
Then fancies flee away!
I'll fear not what men say,
I'll labour night and day
To be a pilgrim.

Percy Dearmer
Adapted from John Bunyan

59   Lead us, heavenly Father, lead us

1   Lead us, heavenly Father, lead us
   O'er the world's tempestuous sea;
   Guard us, guide us, keep us, feed us,
   For we have no help but Thee;
   Yet possessing every blessing,
   If our God our Father be.

2   Saviour, breathe forgiveness o'er us:
   All our weakness Thou dost know;
   Thou didst tread this earth before us,
   Thou didst feel its keenest woe;
   Lone and dreary, faint and weary,
   Through the desert Thou didst go.

3   Spirit of our God, descending,
   Fill our hearts with heavenly joy,
   Love with every passion blending,
   Pleasure that can never cloy;
   Thus provided, pardoned, guided,
   Nothing can our peace destroy.

James Edmeston

60   Mine eyes have seen the glory

1   Mine eyes have seen the glory of the coming of the Lord;
He is trampling out the vintage where the grapes of
    wrath are stored;
He hath loosed the fateful lightning of His terrible
    swift sword:
His truth is marching on.

Glory, glory, alleluia,
Glory, glory, alleluia,
Glory, glory, alleluia,
His truth is marching on.

2   I have seen Him in the watch-fires of a hundred
    circling camps;
They have builded Him an altar in the evening dews
    and damps;
I can read His righteous sentence in the dim and
    flaring lamps:
His day is marching on:

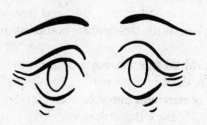

3   I have read a fiery gospel, writ in burnished rows of steel;
     As ye deal with my contemners, so with you my
       grace shall deal;
     Let the hero born of woman crush the serpent with
       his heel:
     Our God is marching on:

4   He has sounded forth the trumpet that shall never call
       retreat;
     He is sifting out the hearts of men before His
       judgement seat;
     O be swift, my soul, to answer Him, be jubilant, my
       feet:
     Our God is marching on:

5   In the beauty of the lilies Christ was born across the
       sea
     With a glory in His bosom that transfigures you and
       me;
     As He died to make men holy, let us die to make
       men free:
     Our God is marching on:

6   He is coming like the glory of the morning on the
       wave;
     He is wisdom to the mighty, He is succour to the
       brave;
     So the world shall be His footstool, and the soul of
       time His slave:
     Our God is marching on:

Mrs Julia Ward Howe

61   O when the saints go marching in

1   O when the saints go marching in,
O when the saints go marching in;
O Lord, I want to be among the number
When the saints go marching in!

2   O when they crown Him Lord of all,
O when they crown Him Lord of all;
O Lord, I want to be among the number
When they crown Him Lord of all.

3   O when all knees bow at His name,
O when all knees bow at His name;
O Lord, I want to be among the number
When all knees bow at His name.

4   O when they sing the Saviour's praise,
O when they sing the Saviour's praise;
O Lord, I want to be among the number
When they sing the Saviour's praise.

5   O when the saints go marching in,
O when the saints go marching in;
O Lord, I want to be among the number
When the saints go marching in!

62   Onward, Christian soldiers

1   Onward, Christian soldiers,
Marching as to war,
With the cross of Jesus
Going on before.
Christ, the royal Master,
Leads against the foe;
Forward into battle,
See, His banners go!

Onward, Christian soldiers,
Marching as to war,
With the cross of Jesus
Going on before.

2   At the sign of triumph
Satan's legions flee;
On, then, Christian soldiers,
On to victory.
Hell's foundations quiver
At the shout of praise;
Brothers, lift your voices,
Loud your anthems raise:

3   Like a mighty army,
Moves the Church of God;
Brothers, we are treading
Where the saints have trod;
We are not divided,
All one body we,
One in hope and doctrine,
One in charity:

4   Crowns and thrones may perish,
    Kingdoms rise and wane,
    But the Church of Jesus
    Constant will remain:
    Gates of hell can never
    'Gainst that Church prevail;
    We have Christ's own promise,
    And that cannot fail:

5   Onward then ye people,
    Join our happy throng;
    Blend with ours your voices
    In the triumph-song;
    'Glory, laud, and honour
    Unto Christ the King!'
    This through countless ages
    Men and angels sing:

S. Baring-Gould

63   Stand up! – stand up for Jesus!

1   Stand up! – stand up for Jesus!
    Ye soldiers of the Cross;
    Lift high His royal banner,
    It must not suffer loss.
    From victory unto victory
    His army He shall lead,
    Till every foe is vanquished,
    And Christ is Lord indeed.

2   Stand up! – stand up for Jesus!
The solemn watchword hear,
If while ye sleep He suffers,
Away with shame and fear,
Where'er ye meet with evil,
Within you or without,
Charge for the God of battles,
And put the foe to rout.

3   Stand up! – stand up for Jesus!
The trumpet call obey,
Forth to the mighty conflict
In this His glorious day.
Ye that are men now serve Him
Against unnumbered foes;
Let courage rise with danger,
And strength to strength oppose.

4   Stand up! – stand up for Jesus!
Stand in His strength alone;
The arm of flesh will fail you,
Ye dare not trust your own.
Put on the Gospel armour,
Each piece put on with prayer;
Where duty calls or danger,
Be never wanting there!

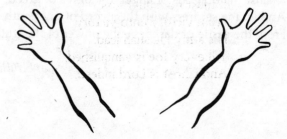

5 Stand up! – stand up for Jesus!
   The strife will not be long;
   This day the noise of battle,
   The next the victor's song.
   To him that overcometh
   A crown of life shall be;
   He with the King of Glory
   Shall reign eternally.

George Duffield

64 When a knight won his spurs

1 When a knight won his spurs in the stories of old,
   He was gentle and brave, he was gallant and bold;
   With a shield on his arm and a lance in his hand,
   For God and for valour he rode through the land.

2 No charger have I, and no sword by my side,
   Yet still to adventure and battle I ride,
   Though back into storyland giants have fled,
   And the knights are no more and the dragons are
       dead.

3 Let faith be my shield and let joy be my steed
   'Gainst the dragons of anger, the ogres of greed;
   And let me set free, with the sword of my youth,
   From the castle of darkness, the power of the truth.

Jan Struther

There Is a Green Hill Far Away

HYMNS FOR LENT AND EASTER

65   On Calvary's tree He died for me

On Calvary's tree He died for me,
That I His love might know;
To set me free He died for me
That's why I love Him so.

A. W. Edsor

66   Ride on! ride on in majesty!

1   Ride on! ride on in majesty!
Hark, all the tribes hosanna cry;
Thine humble beast pursues his road
With palms and scattered garments strowed.

2   Ride on! ride on in majesty!
In lowly pomp ride on to die;
O Christ, Thy triumphs now begin
O'er captive death and conquered sin.

3   Ride on! ride on in majesty!
The wingèd squadrons of the sky
Look down with sad and wondering eyes
To see the approaching sacrifice.

4 Ride on! ride on in majesty!
   Thy last and fiercest strife is nigh;
   The Father, on His sapphire throne,
   Expects His own anointed Son.

5 Ride on! ride on in majesty!
   In lowly pomp ride on to die;
   Bow Thy meek head to mortal pain
   Then take, O God, Thy power, and reign.

Henry Hart Milman

67 There is a green hill far away

1 There is a green hill far away,
   Beside a ruined city wall,
   Where the dear Lord was crucified,
   Who died to save us all.

2 We may not know, we cannot tell,
   What pains He had to bear,
   But we believe it was for us
   He hung and suffered there.

3 He died that we might be forgiven,
   He died to make us good;
   That we might go at last to heaven,
   Saved by His precious blood.

4 There was no other good enough
   To pay the price of sin;
   He only could unlock the gate
   Of heaven, and let us in.

5   O dearly, dearly has He loved,
    And we must love Him too,
    And trust in His redeeming blood,
    And try His works to do.

                    Frances Humphreys

68   When I survey the wondrous Cross

1   When I survey the wondrous Cross,
    Where the young Prince of Glory died,
    My richest gain I count but loss,
    And pour contempt on all my pride.

2   Forbid it, Lord, that I should boast
    Save in the death of Christ my God;
    All the vain things that charm me most,
    I sacrifice them to His blood.

3   See from His head, His hands, His feet,
Sorrow and love flow mingled down;
Did e'er such love and sorrow meet,
Or thorns compose so rich a crown?

4   His dying crimson, like a robe,
Spread o'er His body on the Tree;
Then am I dead to all the globe,
And all the globe is dead to me.

5   Were the whole realm of nature mine,
That were a present far too small;
Love so amazing, so divine,
Demands my soul, my life, my all.

Isaac Watts

69 He is Lord

1   He is Lord,
He is Lord,
He is risen from the dead,
And He is Lord.
Ev'ry knee shall bow,
Ev'ry tongue confess
That Jesus Christ is Lord.

2   He's my Lord,
He's my Lord,
He is risen from the dead,
And He's my Lord.
And my knee shall bow,
And my tongue confess
That Jesus is my Lord.

70   Jesus Christ is risen today

1   Jesus Christ is risen today, *Alleluia!*
    Our triumphant holy day! *Alleluia!*
    Who so lately on the cross *Alleluia!*
    Suffer'd to redeem our loss; *Alleluia!*

2   Haste ye females from your fright, *Alleluia!*
    Take to Galilee your flight. *Alleluia!*
    To His sad disciples say *Alleluia!*
    Jesus Christ is risen today. *Alleluia!*

3   In our Paschal joy and feast *Alleluia!*
    Let our Lord of Life be blest *Alleluia!*
    Let the Holy Trine be praised *Alleluia!*
    And thankful hearts to Heaven be raised. *Alleluia!*

Lyra Davidson

71   Now the green blade rises

1   Now the green blade rises from the buried grain,
    Wheat that in the dark earth many days has lain:
    Love lives again, that with the dead has been:
    Love is come again like wheat that's springing green.

2   In the grave they laid Him, love whom men had slain,
    Thinking that never He would wake again:
    Laid in the earth like grain that sleeps unseen:
    Love is come again like wheat that's springing green.

3   Forth He came at Easter, like the risen grain,
    He that for three days in the grave had lain:
    Live from the dead my risen Lord is seen:
    Love is come again like wheat that's springing green.

4   When our hearts are wintry, grieving or in pain,
    Your touch can call us back to life again:
    Fields of our heart that dead and bare have been:
    Love is come again like wheat that's springing green.

J. M. C. Crum
Adapted by Geoffrey Gardner

72   Thine be the glory

1   Thine be the glory, risen conquering Son,
Endless is the victory Thou o'er death has won;
Angels in bright raiment rolled the stone away.
Kept the folded grave-clothes, where Thy body lay.

Thine be the glory, risen conquering Son,
Endless is the victory Thou o'er death hast won.

2   Lo! Jesus meets us, risen from the tomb;
Lovingly He greets us, scatters fear and gloom;
Let the Church with gladness, hymns of triumph sing,
For her Lord now liveth, death hath lost its sting:

3   No more we doubt Thee, glorious Prince of life;
Life is naught without Thee: aid us in our strife;
Make us more than conquerors, through Thy
    deathless love;
Bring us safe through Jordan to Thy home above:

Edmond L. Budry
Translated by Richard Birch Hoyle

Infant Holy, Infant Lowly

ADVENT HYMNS AND CHRISTMAS CAROLS

73 Hills of the North, rejoice

1 Hills of the North, rejoice:
Rivers and mountain-spring,
Hark to the advent voice!
Valley and lowland, sing!
Though absent long, your Lord is nigh,
He judgement brings, and victory.

2 Isles of the Southern seas,
Deep in your coral caves
Pent be each warring breeze,
Lulled by your restless waves:
He comes to reign with boundless sway,
And make your wastes His great highway.

3 Lands of the East, awake!
Soon shall your sons be free,
The sleep of ages break,
And rise to liberty:
On your far hills, long cold and grey,
Has dawned the everlasting day.

4 Shores of the utmost West,
Ye that have waited long,
Unvisited, unblest,
Break forth to swelling song;
High raise the note, that Jesus died,
Yet lives and reigns – the Crucified!

5   Shout while ye journey home!
Songs be in every mouth! —
Lo, from the North we come,
From East, and West, and South:
City of God, the bonds are free;
We come to live and reign in Thee.

Charles Oakley

74   O come, O come, Emmanuel

1   O come, O come, Emmanuel!
Redeem Thy captive Israel,
That into exile drear is gone
Far from the face of God's dear Son:

*Rejoice! Rejoice! Emmanuel
Shall come to thee, O Israel.*

2   O come, Thou Branch of Jesse! draw
The quarry from the lion's claw;
From the dread caverns of the grave,
From nether hell, Thy people save:

3   O come, O come, Thou Dayspring bright!
Pour on our souls Thy healing light;
Dispel the long night's lingering gloom,
And pierce the shadows of the tomb:

4   O come, Thou Lord of David's key!
The royal door fling wide and free;
Safeguard for us the heavenward road,
And bar the way to death's abode:

5   O come, O come, Adonaï,
     Who in Thy glorious majesty
     From that high mountain clothed with awe
     Gavest Thy folk the elder law:

T. A. Lacey

75   Angels from the realms of glory

1   Angels from the realms of glory,
     Wing your flight o'er all the earth;
     Ye who sang creation's story
     Now proclaim Messiah's birth:

     Gloria in excelsis Deo,
     Gloria in excelsis Deo.

2   Shepherds in the field abiding,
     Watching o'er your flocks by night,
     God with man is now residing;
     Yonder shines the infant Light:

3   Sages, leave your contemplations,
     Brighter visions beam afar;
     Seek the great Desire of Nations,
     Ye have seen His natal star:

4　Saints before the altar bending,
　　Watching long in hope and fear,
　　Suddenly the Lord, descending,
　　In His temple shall appear:

5　Though an infant now we view him,
　　He shall fill His Father's throne,
　　Gather all the nations round Him,
　　Every knee shall then bow down:

J. Montgomery

76　Away in a manger

1　Away in a manger, no crib for a bed,
　The little Lord Jesus laid down His sweet head.
　The stars in the bright sky looked down where He
　　lay,
　The little Lord Jesus asleep on the hay.

2　The cattle are lowing, the Baby awakes,
　But little Lord Jesus no crying He makes.
　I love thee, Lord Jesus! Look down from the sky,
　And stay by my bedside till morning is nigh.

3　Be near me, Lord Jesus; I ask Thee to stay
　Close by me for ever, and love me, I pray.
　Bless all the dear children in Thy tender care,
　And fit us for heaven, to live with Thee there.

77 Ding dong! Merrily on high

1 Ding dong! Merrily on high
In heav'n the bells are ringing.
Ding dong! Verily the sky
Is riv'n with angels singing.

Gloria, Hosanna in excelcis!
Gloria, Hosanna in excelsis!

2 E'en so here below, below,
Let steeple bells be swungen,
And i-o, i-o, i-o,
By priest and people sungen:

3 Pray you, dutifully prime
Your matin chime ye ringers;
May you beautifully rhyme
Your eve-time song, ye singers:

G. R. Woodward

78 Hark! The herald-angels sing

1 Hark! The herald-angels sing,
  'Glory to the new-born King!
  Peace on earth, and mercy mild,
  God and sinners reconciled.'
  Joyful, all you nations, rise,
  Join the triumph of the skies;
  With the angelic host proclaim:
  'Christ is born in Bethlehem!'

  Hark! The herald-angels sing,
  'Glory to the new-born King!'

2 Christ, by highest heaven adored,
  Christ, the everlasting Lord,
  Late in time behold Him come,
  Offspring of a virgin's womb!
  Veiled in flesh the Godhead see!
  Hail, the incarnate Deity!
  Pleased as man with men to dwell,
  Jesus, our Immanuel:

3   Hail, the heaven-born Prince of Peace!
     Hail, the Sun of Righteousness!
     Light and life to all He brings,
     Risen with healing in His wings.
     Mild He lays His glory by,
     Born that man no more may die;
     Born to raise the sons of earth,
     Born to give them second birth:

Charles Wesley
George Whitfield
Martin Madan and others

79   I saw three ships

1   I saw three ships come sailing by,
     On Christmas Day, on Christmas Day,
     I saw three ships come sailing by,
     On Christmas Day in the morning.

2   And what was in those ships all three?
     On Christmas Day, on Christmas Day,
     And what was in those ships all three?
     On Christmas Day in the morning.

3   Our Saviour Christ and His lady,
On Christmas Day, on Christmas Day,
Our Saviour Christ and His lady,
On Christmas Day in the morning.

4   Pray, whither sail'd those ships all three?
On Christmas Day, on Christmas Day,
Pray, whither sail'd those ships all three?
On Christmas Day in the morning.

5   Oh, they sail'd into Bethlehem,
On Christmas Day, on Christmas Day,
Oh, they sail'd into Bethlehem,
On Christmas Day in the morning.

6   And all the bells on earth shall ring,
On Christmas Day, on Christmas Day,
And all the bells on earth shall ring,
On Christmas Day in the morning.

7   And all the angels in heav'n shall sing,
On Christmas Day, on Christmas Day,
And all the angels in heav'n shall sing,
On Christmas Day in the morning.

8   And all the souls on earth shall sing,
On Christmas Day, on Christmas Day,
And all the souls on earth shall sing,
On Christmas Day in the morning.

80   Infant holy

1   Infant holy,
    Infant lowly,
    For His bed a cattle stall;
    Oxen lowing,
    Little knowing
    Christ the Babe is Lord of all.
    Swift are winging
    Angels singing,
    Nowells ringing,
    Tidings bringing,
    Christ the Babe is Lord of all.
    Christ the Babe is Lord of all.

2   Flocks were sleeping,
    Shepherds keeping
    Vigil till the morning new.
    Saw the glory,
    Heard the story,
    Tidings of a gospel true.
    Thus rejoicing,
    Free from sorrow,
    Praises voicing,
    Greet the morrow,
    Christ the Babe was born for you!
    Christ the Babe was born for you!

Translated by E. M. G. Reed

81   In the bleak mid-winter

1   In the bleak mid-winter
    Frosty wind made moan,
    Earth stood hard as iron,
    Water like a stone;
    Snow had fallen, snow on snow,
    Snow on snow,
    In the bleak mid-winter,
    Long ago.

2   Our God, heaven cannot hold Him
    Nor earth sustain;
    Heaven and earth shall flee away
    When He comes to reign:
    In the bleak mid-winter
    A stable-place sufficed
    The Lord God Almighty,
    Jesus Christ.

3   Enough for Him, whom cherubim
    Worship night and day,
    A breastful of milk,
    And a mangerful of hay;
    Enough for Him, whom angels
    Fall down before,
    The ox and ass and camel
    Which adore.

4   Angels and archangels
     May have gathered there,
     Cherubim and seraphim
     Thronged the air:
     But only His mother
     In her maiden bliss
     Worshipped the Belovèd
     With a kiss.

5   What can I give Him,
     Poor as I am?
     If I were a shepherd
     I would bring a lamb;
     If I were a wise man
     I would do my part;
     Yet what I can I give Him –
     Give my heart.

Christina Rossetti

82   O little town of Bethlehem

1   O little town of Bethlehem,
     How still we see you lie!
     Above your deep and dreamless sleep
     The silent stars go by:
     Yet in your dark streets shining
     Is everlasting Light;
     The hopes and fears of all the years
     Are met in you tonight.

2   For Christ is born of Mary;
And, gathered all above
While mortals sleep, the angels keep
Their watch of wondering love.
O morning stars, together
Proclaim the holy birth,
And praises sing to God the King,
And peace to men on earth.

3   How silently, how silently,
The wondrous gift is given!
So God imparts to human hearts
The blessings of His heaven.
No ear may hear His coming;
But in this world of sin,
Where meek souls will receive Him, still
The dear Christ enters in.

4   O holy child of Bethlehem,
Descend to us, we pray;
Cast out our sin, and enter in;
Be born in us today.
We hear the Christmas angels
The great glad tidings tell;
O come to us, abide with us,
Our Lord Immanuel.

Phillips Brooks

83 Once in royal David's city

1 Once in royal David's city,
Stood a lowly cattle shed,
Where a mother laid her Baby,
In a manger for His bed.
Mary was that mother mild,
Jesus Christ her little child.

2 He came down to earth from heaven,
Who is God and Lord of all,
And His shelter was a stable,
And His cradle was a stall:
With the poor and mean and lowly
Lived on earth our Saviour holy.

3 And through all his wondrous childhood
He would honour and obey,
Love and watch the lowly mother,
In whose gentle arms He lay.
Christian children all should be
Kind, obedient, good as He.

4 For He is our childhood's pattern:
Day by day like us He grew;
He was little, weak, and helpless;
Tears and smiles like us He knew:
And He feels for all our sadness,
And He shares in all our gladness.

5 And our eyes at last shall see Him
   Through His own redeeming love;
   For that Child, so dear and gentle,
   Is our Lord in heaven above;
   And He leads His children on
   To the place where He is gone.

6 Not in that poor, lowly stable,
   With the oxen standing by,
   We shall see Him, but in heaven,
   Set at God's right hand on high;
   There His children gather round
   Bright like stars, with glory crowned.

Cecil Francis Alexander

84 Rocking carol

1 Little Jesus, sweetly sleep, do not stir;
   We will lend a coat of fur;
   We will rock You, rock You, rock You,
   We will rock You, rock You, rock You;
   See the fur to keep You warm,
   Snugly round Your tiny form.

2 Mary's little baby, sleep, sweetly sleep,
   Sleep in comfort, slumber deep;
   We will rock You, rock You, rock You,
   We will rock You, rock You, rock You;
   We will serve You all we can,
   Darling, darling little man.

Translated by Percy Dearmer

85   See amid the winter's snow

1   See amid the winter's snow,
    Born for us on earth below,
    See, the Lamb of God appears,
    Promised from eternal years.

   Hail, thou ever blessèd morn!
   Hail, redemption's happy dawn!
   Sing through all Jerusalem:
   Christ is born in Bethlehem!

2   Lo, within a manger lies
    He who built the starry skies,
    He who, throned in height sublime,
    Sits amid the cherubim:

3   Say, ye holy shepherds, say,
    What your joyful news today;
    Wherefore have ye left your sheep
    On the lonely mountain steep?:

4   As we watched at dead of night,
    Lo, we saw a wondrous light:
    Angels, singing peace on earth,
    Told us of the Saviour's birth:

5   Sacred Infant, all divine,
    What a tender love was Thine,
    Thus to come from highest bliss
    Down to such a world as this!:

6   Teach, O teach us, holy Child,
By Thy face so meek and mild,
Teach us to resemble Thee
In Thy sweet humility:

Edward Caswall

86   Silent night

1   Silent night, holy night!
Sleeps the world; hid from sight,
Mary and Joseph in stable bare
Watched o'er the Child beloved and fair
Sleeping in heavenly rest,
Sleeping in heavenly rest.

2   Silent night, holy night!
Shepherds first saw the light;
Heard resounding clear and long,
Far and near, the angel song:
'Christ the Redeemer is here,'
'Christ the Redeemer is here.'

3   Silent night, holy night!
Son of God, O how bright
Love is smiling from Your face!
Strikes for us now the hour of grace,
Saviour, since You are born,
Saviour, since You are born.

J. Mohr

87   The Coventry carol

Lully, lulla, thou little tiny child;
By, by, lully, lullay.

1   O sisters two,
How may we do
For to preserve this day
This poor youngling
For whom we do sing
By, by, lully lullay?

2   Herod the king,
In his raging,
Chargèd he hath this day
His men of might,
In his own sight
All young children to slay.

3   That woe is me,
Poor child, for thee,
And ever mourn, and say:
For thy parting
Neither say nor sing
By, by, lully lullay.

Pageant of the Shearmen and Tailors

88   The holly and the ivy

1   The holly and the ivy,
When they are both full grown;
Of all the trees that are in the wood,
The holly bears the crown.

The rising of the sun,
And the running of the deer,
The playing of the merry organ,
Sweet singing in the choir.

2 The holly bears a blossom,
As white as the lily flower;
And Mary bore sweet Jesus Christ
To be our sweet Saviour:

3 The holly bears a berry,
As red as any blood;
And Mary bore sweet Jesus Christ
To do poor sinners good:

4 The holly bears a prickle,
As sharp as any thorn;
And Mary bore sweet Jesus Christ
On Christmas Day in the morn:

5 The holly bears a bark,
As bitter as any gall;
And Mary bore sweet Jesus Christ
For to redeem us all:

6 The holly and the ivy,
When they are both full grown;
Of all the trees that are in the wood,
The holly bears the crown:

Traditional

89   Unto us a Boy is born!

1   Unto us a Boy is born!
King of all creation,
Came He to a world forlorn
The Lord of every nation,
The Lord of every nation.

2   Cradled in a stall was He
With sleepy cows and asses;
But the very beasts could see
That He all men surpasses,
That He all men surpasses.

3   Herod then with fear was filled:
'A prince,' he said, 'in Jewry!'
All the little boys he killed
At Bethlehem in his fury,
At Bethlehem in his fury.

4   Now may Mary's Son, who came
So long ago to love us,
Lead us all with hearts aflame
Unto the joys above us,
Unto the joys above us.

5   Alpha and Omega He!
Let the organ thunder,
While the choir with peals of glee
Doth rend the air asunder!
Doth rend the air asunder!

Translated by Percy Dearmer

90   We three kings of Orient are

1   We three kings of Orient are;
    Bearing gifts we traverse afar
    Field and fountain, moor and mountain,
    Following yonder star.

O star of wonder, star of night,
Star with royal beauty bright,
Westward leading, still proceeding,
Guide us to thy perfect light.

2   Born a king on Bethlehem plain,
    Gold I bring, to crown Him again,
    King for ever, ceasing never,
    Over us all to reign:

3   Frankincense to offer have I,
    Incense owns a deity nigh;
    Prayer and praising, all men raising,
    Worship Him, God most high:

4   Myrrh is mine; its bitter perfume
    Breathes a life of gathering gloom;
    Sorrowing, sighing, bleeding, dying,
    Sealed in the stone-cold tomb:

5   Glorious now behold Him arise,
    King and God and sacrifice,
    Alleluia, alleluia,
    Earth to the heav'ns replies:

John Henry Hopkins

Index of first lines

Hymn No.		Page No.
15	All creatures of our God and King	29
39	All people that on earth do dwell	59
16	*All things bright and beautiful*	31
27	Amazing grace! how sweet the sound	45
75	Angels from the realms of glory	107
42	And did those feet in ancient time	63
40	At the name of Jesus	60
76	Away in a manger, no crib for a bed	108
41	Clap your hands all you people	62
54	Colours of day dawn into the mind	79
17	Come, ye thankful people, come	32
18	Daisies are our silver	34
77	Ding dong! Merrily on high	109
28	Father, hear the prayer we offer	46
1	Father, we thank Thee for the night	13
55	Fight the good fight with all thy might	80
29	Firmly I believe and truly	47
19	For the beauty of the earth	36
2	From the rising of the sun	13
8	Gentle Jesus, meek and mild	20
56	Give me oil in my lamp, keep me burning	81
3	Glory to You, my God, this night	14
57	*Go, tell it on the mountain*	83
49	God save our gracious Queen	71
20	God who made the earth	37
78	Hark! The herald-angels sing	110
69	He is Lord	98

125

58	He who would valiant be	84
21	*He's got the whole world in His hand*	38
73	Hills of the North, rejoice	105
45	I danced in the morning	66
79	I saw three ships come sailing by	111
50	I vow to thee, my country, all earthly things above	72
4	If I had a hammer, I'd hammer in the morning	15
80	Infant holy	113
81	In the bleak mid-winter	114
70	Jesus Christ is risen today, *Alleluia!*	99
9	Jesus, friend of little children	21
10	Jesus, good above all other	22
11	Jesus loves me! this I know	22
43	*Joshua fit the battle of Jericho*	63
12	Just as I am, Your child to be	23
30	Kum ba yah, my Lord, Kum ba yah	48
59	Lead us, heavenly Father, lead us	85
44	Let all the world in ev'ry corner sing	64
22	Let us, with a gladsome mind	39
84	Little Jesus, sweetly sleep, do not stir	118
31	Lord Jesus Christ	48
5	Lord of all hopefulness, Lord of all joy	16
32	Loving Shepherd of Thy sheep	50
87	Lully, lulla, thou little tiny child	121
60	Mine eyes have seen the glory of the coming of the Lord	86
23	Morning has broken	40
46	Now thank we all our God	68
6	Now the day is over	17

71	Now the green blade rises from the buried grain	101
74	O come, O come, Emmanuel!	106
82	O little town of Bethlehem	115
61	O when the saints go marching in	88
48	*Oh! Oh! Oh! how good is the Lord*	70
65	On Calvary's tree He died for me	95
83	Once in royal David's city	117
62	Onward, Christian soldiers	89
37	Our Father, who art in heaven	55
33	Praise God from whom all blessings flow	50
13	Praise Him, praise Him, all you little children	24
47	Praise, my soul, the King of heaven	69
35	Put your hand in the hand of the man	53
66	Ride on! ride on in majesty!	95
85	See amid the winter's snow	119
86	Silent night, holy night!	120
63	Stand up! – stand up for Jesus!	90
51	Tell out, my soul, the greatness of the Lord	73
24	Thank you for the world so sweet	41
88	The holly and the ivy	121
14	The ink is black, the page is white	25
36	The King of love my Shepherd is	54
34	The Lord's my Shepherd, I'll not want	51
52	The wise man built his house upon the rock	74
67	There is a green hill far away	96
72	Thine be the glory, risen conquering Son	102
25	Twinkle, twinkle, little star	41
89	Unto us a Boy is born!	123
26	We plough the fields, and scatter	42

90   We three kings of Orient are   124

64   When a knight won his spurs in the stories of
         old   92

38   When I needed a neighbour, were you there,
         were you there?   56

68   When I survey the wondrous Cross   97

53   When Israel was in Egypt's land   75

 7   When lamps are lighted in the town   18

Acknowledgements

The publishers gratefully acknowledge permission to reproduce copyright material in this book:

'Black and White' by Earl Robinson and David Arkin © Durham Music Limited. International Copyright secured. All rights reserved. Used by permission; 'Clap your hands' by Jimmy Owens copyright © 1991 Lexicon Music Inc. and Universal Songs BV, administered by United Nation's Music Publishers Ltd. All rights reserved. Used by permission; 'Colours of day' by Sue McClellan, Keith Rycroft and John Pac copyright © 1974 Thankyou Music, PO Box 75, Eastbourne, East Sussex BN23 6NW, UK. Used by permission; 'Daisies are our silver' by Jan Struther (1901–53) from *Enlarged Songs of Praise 1931* by permission of Oxford University Press; 'Father, we thank Thee' reproduced from *New Child Songs* (Denholm House Press, 1973) with the permission of the National Christian Education Council; 'From the rising of the sun' by Paul Deming copyright © Integrity's Hosanna! Music PO Box 101, Eastbourne, East Sussex BN21 3UX, UK. All rights reserved. International Copyright secured. Used by permission; 'Glory to You, my God, this night' words: T. Ken, Revised *Hymns for Today's Church, 1982* copyright © 1982 by Hope Publishing Co., Carol Stream IL 60188. All rights reserved. Used by permission; 'God who made the earth' by S. B. Rhodes reprinted from *Junior Praise* (Marshall Pickering, 1986) copyright © 1986, P. Horrobin and G. Leavers, by permission of P. Horrobin; 'If I had a hammer' by Pete Seeger and Lee Hays © TRO Essex Music Limited. International Copyright secured. All rights reserved. Used by permission; 'Just as I am' by Marianne Farningham reprinted from *Junior Praise* (Marshall Pickering, 1986) copyright © 1986, P. Horrobin and G. Leavers, by permission of P. Horrobin; 'Lord Jesus Christ' by Patrick Appleford © 1960 Josef Weinberger Limited. Reproduced by permission of the copyright owners; 'Lord of all hopefulness, Lord of all joy' by Jan Struther (1901–53) from *Enlarged Songs of Praise 1931* by permission of Oxford University Press; 'Lord of the Dance' by Sydney Carter © Stainer and Bell Ltd, London, England. Reproduced by permission; 'Morning has broken' by Eleanor Farjeon reprinted from *The Children's Bells* (Oxford University Press) copyright © Eleanor Farjeon by permission of David Higham Associates; 'Now the day is over' by S. Baring-Gould reprinted from *Junior Praise* (Marshall Pickering, 1986) copyright © 1986 P. Horrobin and G. Leavers, by permission of P. Horrobin; 'On Calvary's tree' by A. W. Edsor, words copyright © Kingsway Publications Ltd/Thankyou Music, PO Box 75, Eastbourne, East Sussex BN23 6NW, UK. Used by permission; 'Put your hand in the hand' by Gene MacLellan copyright © 1970 Beechwood Music of Canada, Ardmore and Beechwood Ltd, London WC2H 0EA/International Music Publications. Used by permission; 'When a knight won his spurs' by Jan Struther (1901–53) from *Enlarged Songs of Praise 1931* by permission of Oxford University Press; 'When I needed a neighbour' by Sydney Carter © Stainer and Bell Ltd, London, England. Reproduced by permission; 'When Israel was in Egypt's land' a Negro spiritual adapted by Peter D. Smith © 1967 Stainer and Bell Ltd, London, England. Reproduced by permission.

Every effort has been made to trace copyright holders, but in a few cases this has proved impossible. The editor and publishers apologize for these cases of unwilling copyright transgression and would like to hear from any copyright holders not acknowledged.